It's your turn, SNOOPY

by CHARLES M. SCHULZ

Selected cartoons from
*YOU'RE THE GUEST OF HONOR,
CHARLIE BROWN*, Vol. 1

A FAWCETT CREST BOOK

Fawcett Publications, I__ Greenwich, Conn__ ecticut

IT'S YOUR TURN, SNOOPY

This book prepared especially for Fawcett Publications, Inc.,
comprises the first half of YOU'RE THE GUEST OF HONOR,
CHARLIE BROWN, and is reprinted by arrangement with
Holt, Rinehart and Winston, Inc.

Copyright © 1972, 1973 by United Feature Syndicate, Inc.

ISBN: 0-449-23021-X

Printed in the United States of America

7 6 5 4 3 2 1

It's your turn, SNOOPY

WHAT DO YOU DO WITH TWO FRIENDS WHO ARE HAVING A MISUNDERSTANDING?

STRAIGHTEN THEM OUT! SHOW 'EM WHERE THEY'VE GONE WRONG!! TELL 'EM TO SHAPE UP!!!

IS THAT GOOD PSYCHOLOGY?

IN STRICT MEDICAL TERMS, IT'S CALLED "BUTTING IN"!

IT HAS BEEN FORTY-FIVE MINUTES SINCE I FIRST CAME INTO SCHOOL THIS MORNING...

I FIND, UNFORTUNATELY, THAT I AM NOT ANY SMARTER NOW THAN WHEN I ARRIVED....IF IT IS TRUE THAT NATURE ABHORS A VACUUM, I MAY EVEN BE A LITTLE DUMBER!! NOW, THEREFORE, I WOULD LIKE TO...

YES, MA'AM?

RATS! I HAD A PRETTY GOOD SPEECH GOING THERE FOR A MINUTE!

YOU KNOW WHAT?

IF WE'RE GOING TO HAVE A TESTIMONIAL DINNER FOR CHARLIE BROWN, IT SHOULD BE A SURPRISE..

THAT'S RIGHT...HE SHOULDN'T KNOW ABOUT IT...

LET'S NOT EVEN INVITE HIM!

HELLO, PEPPERMINT PATTY? WE'RE THINKING ABOUT HAVING A TESTIMONIAL DINNER FOR CHARLIE BROWN.. COULD YOU COME?

WHAT HAPPENS AT A TESTIMONIAL DINNER?

WELL, EVERYONE GETS UP, AND SAYS ALL SORTS OF THINGS ABOUT WHAT A GREAT PERSON THE GUEST OF HONOR IS...

IT'S GOING TO BE A QUIET EVENING!

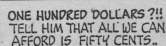

WE'VE ADDRESSED A LOT OF INVITATIONS, HAVEN'T WE, SIR?

I THINK I'M GETTING SICK FROM LICKING ALL THESE STAMPS AND ENVELOPES

BY GOLLY, THAT STUPID CHUCK BETTER APPRECIATE ALL THE WORK WE'RE DOING TO GIVE HIM THIS TESTIMONIAL DINNER..BESIDES, HE'S A TERRIBLE BALL PLAYER...

IF WE DON'T BELIEVE IN WHAT WE'RE DOING, AREN'T WE BEING HYPOCRITICAL, SIR?

I HATE QUESTIONS LIKE THAT!

SCHULZ

THERE'S STILL QUITE A BIT OF WORK TO DO ON THE TESTIMONIAL DINNER...

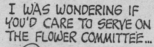

I WAS WONDERING IF YOU'D CARE TO SERVE ON THE FLOWER COMMITTEE...

SO MUCH FOR THE FLOWER COMMITTEE!

WELCO CANCEL THE DINNER?

WE CAN'T CANCEL THE DINNER!! EVERYONE IS ALREADY HERE! EVERYONE IS ALREADY SEATED! EVEN THE GUEST OF HONOR IS HERE!!

IT'S ALL HYPOCRITICAL...WE'RE NOT REALLY SINCERE...WE'RE ALL GOING TO SAY THINGS ABOUT CHARLIE BROWN THAT WE DON'T REALLY BELIEVE, AND IT'S ALL HYPOCRITICAL!

I WOULD HAVE ENJOYED EVEN A HYPOCRITICAL DINNER

→

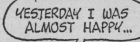

"A PINCH-HITTER MAY BE DESIGNATED TO BAT FOR THE STARTING PITCHER AND ALL SUBSEQUENT PITCHERS IN ANY GAME WITHOUT OTHERWISE AFFECTING THE STATUS OF THE PITCHERS IN THE GAME.."

" FAILURE TO DESIGNATE A PINCH-HITTER PRIOR TO THE GAME PRECLUDES THE USE OF A DESIGNATED PINCH-HITTER FOR THE GAME ... PINCH-HITTERS FOR A DESIGNATED PINCH-HITTER MAY BE USED..."

"ANY SUBSTITUTE PINCH-HITTER FOR A DESIGNATED PINCH-HITTER HIMSELF BECOMES A DESIGNATED PINCH-HITTER... A REPLACED DESIGNATED PINCH-HITTER SHALL NOT RE-ENTER THE GAME "

I PROBABLY WON'T GET TO BAT THE WHOLE SEASON...

SCHULZ

→

Dear Dog, This is to inform you that you are one of the finalists for this year's Daisy Hill Puppy Cup Award.

THE DAISY HILL PUPPY CUP!! I'VE BEEN NOMINATED FOR THE DAISY HILL PUPPY CUP!!!

WHEEEEEE!

STUPID BEAGLE!

HERE ARE SOME MORE RULES ABOUT THE DAISY HILL PUPPY CUP AWARD

"EACH NOMINEE MUST SUBMIT FIVE LETTERS FROM INTERESTED PARTIES STATING WHY HE SHOULD BE NAMED 'THE NEIGHBORHOOD DOG OF THE YEAR'"

DON'T ASK ME TO WRITE A LETTER FOR YOU! I WOULDN'T RECOMMEND YOU FOR "DOG OF THE MINUTE"!

WHAAH!

AND CRYING WON'T HELP!!

I THINK THEY'RE GOING TO ANNOUNCE THE WINNER OF THE DAISY HILL PUPPY CUP TOMORROW

DOES SNOOPY THINK HE HAS A CHANCE? IS HE CONFIDENT?

OH, YES... HE'S VERY CONFIDENT...

WHY ELSE WOULD HE BE BUILDING A TROPHY CASE?

WHEN YOU'VE LOST AT SOMETHING, YOU CAN REACT IN TWO WAYS...

ONE WAY IS TO ANALYZE JUST WHY YOU LOST...TRY TO FIGURE OUT WHAT YOUR WEAKNESSES WERE, AND THEN TRY TO IMPROVE SO THAT NEXT TIME YOU CAN WIN..

BLEAH!

THAT'S THE OTHER WAY!

BAM! BAM! BAM!

YOUR HUNGER STRIKE DIDN'T LAST VERY LONG, DID IT?

I LEARNED SOMETHING..

THE BRAIN MAY BE IMPORTANT..

..BUT THE STOMACH IS STILL IN CHARGE!

PAT
PAT
PAT

WHAT IN THE WORLD ARE YOU DOING?

PAT
PAT

PATTING BIRDS ON THE HEAD... I HAVE FOUND THAT WHENEVER I GET REALLY DEPRESSED, PATTING BIRDS ON THE HEAD CHEERS ME UP...

YOU JUST THINK YOU'RE CUTE BECAUSE YOU'RE CUTE!

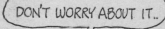

He was a very rich cowboy.

He had a car and a horse.

He kept his car in the carport....

And he kept his horse in the horseport.

POW!

CHARLIE BROWN, THIS IS MY BROTHER, "RERUN"... CAN HE BE ON OUR TEAM?

A LITTLE KID LIKE THAT?

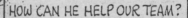

HOW CAN HE HELP OUR TEAM?

HE DOESN'T SMOKE!

OKAY, RERUN, THIS IS OUR FIRST GAME OF THE SEASON

I'M GOING TO LET YOU START IN LEFT FIELD AS A FAVOR TO YOUR SISTER...

JUST DO THE BEST YOU CAN, AND TRY NOT TO GET KILLED BY A FLY BALL!

WHAT ARE WE PLAYING FOR; THE STANLEY CUP?

SCHULZ

HEY, MANAGER, MY GLOVE IS SO STIFF I CAN'T CATCH THE BALL!

THAT'S BECAUSE YOU HAVEN'T USED IT ALL WINTER...TRY RUBBING A LITTLE NEAT'S-FOOT OIL INTO IT

FORGET IT!

I HATE ANY SPORT WHERE YOU HAVE TO TAKE CARE OF YOUR EQUIPMENT!

SCHULZ

HEY, MANAGER, I WAS JUST WONDERING IF...

THIS IS RIDICULOUS!! HOW CAN I PITCH A BALL GAME WITH PEOPLE COMING UP TO ME ALL THE TIME WITH QUESTIONS?

YOU NEED A SECRETARY, CHARLIE BROWN... YOU NEED SOMEONE TO SCREEN YOUR CALLERS...

I'M SORRY... OUR MANAGER CAN'T SEE YOU NOW... HE'S BUSY PITCHING!

I CAN'T STAND IT...

WE WON! WE WON, CHARLIE BROWN!!

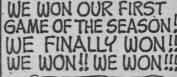

WE WON OUR FIRST GAME OF THE SEASON! WE FINALLY WON!! WE WON!! WE WON!!!

I THINK I'M GOING TO CRY..

WE WON, CHARLIE BROWN! C'MON, LET'S GO HOME, AND CELEBRATE!

NO! FIRST I HAVE TO WAIT FOR THE OPPOSING MANAGER TO COME OVER AND CONGRATULATE ME

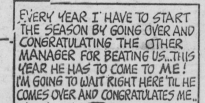

EVERY YEAR I HAVE TO START THE SEASON BY GOING OVER AND CONGRATULATING THE OTHER MANAGER FOR BEATING US...THIS YEAR HE HAS TO COME TO ME! I'M GOING TO WAIT RIGHT HERE 'TIL HE COMES OVER AND CONGRATULATES ME...

YES, SIR; I'M THE TEAM MANAGER AND THIS IS OUR SECOND BASEMAN, LINUS VAN PELT..

AND YOU'RE THE LEAGUE PRESIDENT? WE'RE VERY GLAD TO KNOW YOU, SIR

YOU HAVE A VERY NICE BICYCLE REPAIR SHOP HERE

ONE OF MY GREAT REGRETS IS THAT I NEVER GOT TO MEET JUDGE KENESAW MOUNTAIN LANDIS!

RERUN, YOU REALLY LET ME DOWN!

I WAS THE ONE WHO TALKED CHARLIE BROWN INTO LETTING YOU PLAY; SO THEN YOU GO AND GET US INVOLVED IN A BETTING SCANDAL!

I ONLY BET A NICKEL...WHAT ELSE CAN YOU DO WITH A NICKEL THESE DAYS?

OF COURSE, I MUST ADMIT ONE THING...

YOU'RE THE FIRST PERSON WHO EVER HAD THE COURAGE TO BET ON CHARLIE BROWN'S TEAM

I'LL DRINK TO THAT!

HE'S COMING! HE'S COMING!

THANK YOU, EASTER BEAGLE! THANK YOU!

THANK YOU

THANK YOU VERY MUCH

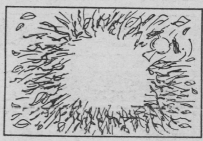

ACTUALLY, WOODSTOCK PROBABLY SHOULDN'T HAVE A PAPER DELIVERED TO HIS HOME..

SCHULZ

THE PEANUTS GALLERY

includes:

THAT'S LIFE, SNOOPY   22886-X
  (selected cartoons from *Thompson Is In Trouble,
  Charlie Brown,* Vol. 2)

YOU'VE COME A LONG WAY, SNOOPY   M2838
  (selected cartoons from *Thompson Is In Trouble,
  Charlie Brown,* Vol. 1)

YOU'VE GOT TO BE YOU, SNOOPY   M2705
  (selected cartoons from *You've Come a Long Way,
  Charlie Brown,* Vol. 2)

IT'S ALL YOURS, SNOOPY   M2596
  (selected cartoons from *You've Come a Long Way,
  Charlie Brown,* Vol. 1)

95¢ Wherever Paperbacks Are Sold